Activities for the Family Caregiver

FRONTOTEMPORAL DEMENTIA / FRONTAL LOBE DEMENTIA / PICK'S DISEASE

HOW TO ENGAGE
HOW TO LIVE

Scott Silknitter
Robert D. Brennan, RN, NHA, MS, CDP
Vanessa Emm, BA, AC-BC, ACC/EDU, CDP

Disclaimer

This book is for informational purposes only and is not intended as medical advice, diagnosis, or treatment. Always seek advice from a qualified physician about medical concerns, and do not disregard medical advice because of something you may read within this book. This book does not replace the need for diagnostic evaluation, ongoing physician care, and professional assessment of treatments. Every effort has been made to make this book as complete and helpful as possible. It is important, however, for this book to be used as a resource and idea-generating guide and not as an ultimate source for a plan of care.

ISBN 978-1-943285-16-7

Published by
R.O.S. Therapy Systems, L.L.C.
Greensboro, NC
888-352-9788
www.ROSTherapySystems.com

Activities for the Family Caregiver— Frontotemporal Dementia

My mission is to improve quality of life for caregivers and their loved one. It started with a simple backyard project to help my father and mother during a 25-year fight with Parkinson's and dementia. It has grown into a company that has attracted experts that have joined our mission.

This book is designed for family caregivers. The purpose is to provide a resource for caregivers regarding activities of daily living, engagement, safety and general information. A step up from *Activities 101 for the Family Caregiver—Frontotemporal Dementia*, it is based on the principles and instruction provided to long-term care staffs in various settings.

We have written this book with the assistance of Robert D. Brennan, RN, NHA, MS, CDP, and Vanessa Emm, BA, ACC/EDU, AC-BC, CDP, who have been working in long-term care for a combination of 60 years. Our goal is to provide helpful information on caregiving, activities of daily living, and engagement based on the Four Pillars of Activities.

We hope you find this book useful. We encourage you to have other family members and caregivers read this to allow for consistency with approaches, verbal cues, physical assistance and modifications that produce positive results for your loved one.

From our family of caregivers to yours, please remember that you are not alone, and to never give up.

Scott Silknitter

Family Members and Caregivers
that have read this book:

_____

_____

_____

_____

_____

_____

_____

_____

_____

_____

_____

Table of Contents

Chapter 1

Frontotemporal Dementia Overview

With frontotemporal dementia, the more you know and understand, the more you will recognize the changes occurring in your loved one's world and what they no longer have control over.

Keep in mind to concentrate and celebrate what your loved one **CAN DO** and **CAN UNDERSTAND** at any given time, not what they CANNOT!!

Frontotemporal dementia (FTD) is also commonly known as frontal lobe dementia, Pick's disease, and "The Terse and Curse" dementia. FTD is caused by the disease process known as frontotemporal lobar degeneration (FTLD).

Individuals can have both frontotemporal dementia and other types of dementia such as Alzheimer's.

This is a physical illness, as with other forms of dementia, but may also mimic symptoms of mental illness.

This condition has very specific symptoms, characteristics, and behaviors because of the areas of the brain that are affected. It may be difficult to diagnosis because the symptoms are similar to those of other physical impairments.

Frontotemporal dementia affects your loved one's personality, behavior, language, communication ability, and motor skills.

Unlike Alzheimer's and other forms of dementia, the primary areas of the brain affected are the frontal and temporal lobes of the brain.

It is important to understand that unlike other dementias, memory loss and disorientation does not occur first with frontotemporal dementia.

Frontal Lobe

Functions of the frontal lobe include:

- The control center for our emotions
- Insight and judgment
- Governing our mood and behavior
- Home of our personality
- Social appropriateness
- Language
- Motor functions
- Ability for planning, sequencing, and prioritizing activities

Temporal Lobe

Functions of the temporal lobe include:

- Language
- Understanding words, speaking, reading, writing, and connecting words with their meanings to form sentences
- Emotions

As with all forms of dementia, your loved one did not choose to have frontotemporal dementia. You did not choose to become a caregiver. But both happened and you must be prepared to adapt to the changes occurring in your loved one.

Accuracy of Diagnosis

It is extremely important to you and your loved one that an accurate diagnosis is obtained. Your loved one's physician may not be familiar with this type of dementia.

Because of the diversity of symptoms, and memory loss not being one of the first symptoms, the diagnosis of frontotemporal dementia may be difficult to identify.

Characteristics of Frontotemporal Dementia

As previously stated memory loss is not the first symptom presented.

Changes in personality, behavior, and motor skills are usually the first symptoms and can begin as young as age 45.

The progression of frontotemporal dementia is faster than Alzheimer's.

There are several symptoms that your loved one may exhibit during the progression of this form of dementia. Some of the most common are:

Complications with Completing Tasks

- Inability to complete common/familiar tasks and not realize there is a problem

- Inability to continue working, inability to do a job

- Trouble with organizing work or projects

- Difficulty prioritizing, paying bills, and/or ability to multitask

- Exhibition of frustration and/or anger toward common tasks

Difficulty with Communication

Communication skills and abilities can change significantly. Some examples of this are:

- Cannot find the "right" words to describe something very familiar, e.g., use of the word "horse" when describing a car on the road

- Inability to write common words or to complete sentences

- Inability to write thoughts down on paper

- Difficulty in expressing emotions verbally

- Difficulty sorting thoughts and being able to recall information

Poor Judgment

Judgment will be negatively affected by frontotemporal dementia. For example, your loved one might make choices that put their safety at risk. Some examples of this include:

- Being out in the cold without a jacket or shoes

- Leaving a gas stove on without a flame ignited on burner

- Inappropriate comments, possibly sexual in nature, acting inappropriately with coworkers or family members

- Putting their hand in a boiling liquid, not realizing it is hot

Difficulty Planning and Organizing

- Inability to plan a project or meeting at work

- Difficulty planning an appropriate meal for the time of day

- Difficulty with daily decision making

- Difficulty making dinner or lunch
  - Deciding what to eat
  - Not understanding what a spice is by name
  - Cannot turn the stove on

Changes in Motor Skills
(not seen before due to other health issues)

- Poor balance

- Difficulty walking, gait disorder

- Muscle rigidity, body stiffness

- Trouble with eye movement (closing of eyelids with difficulty opening)

- Tremors

- Inability to manipulate or hold small objects

Decreased Ability to Reason

- Problems with abstract thinking

- Cannot determine an appropriate action, e.g., unable to pay the bill and tip at a restaurant

- Can no longer calculate; such as adding, dividing, multiplying

- Difficulty with problem solving

- Inability to comprehend others' viewpoints and vocalizations

Changes in Personality

- Becomes self-centered
  - Decreased awareness of how behaviors impact others
  - Primary focus on self
  - Centered on own needs above others, e.g., "I want/need this now."

- Increased irritability, anxiety, aggression
  - Verbal and physical aggression at sporadic times
  - Increased sense of worry and irritation
  - Issues related to various scenarios that are unseen by the caregiver

- Curses and uses foul language
  - Verbal abuse, often times "out of character"

- Foul language toward those providing care can be expressed with no understanding or reasoning of the situation at hand

- Complains and criticizes more
  - Out of the ordinary complaints
  - Uncharacteristic critical statements

- Decreased motivation
  - Loss of interest and motivation for activities that they used to engage in
  - Lack of motivation to start an activity/task, e.g., not assisting with activities of daily living such as bathing, toileting, and dressing

- Decreased inhibition
  - Nudity and masturbation
  - Less caution with day-to-day tasks

- Becomes tearful or upset easily
  - Tearfulness while watching a commercial on TV or listening to a story

- o Unrest while waiting for meal preparation, having to wait their turn during a game, or when waiting their turn for the restroom

- Says or does things they never would have done before
  - o Verbal outbursts
  - o Impulsive behavior, e.g., gorging on food, taking food from another person
  - o Taking clothes off inappropriately

As a caregiver, it will help if you remind yourself, "It is the disease, not my loved one, that is causing these changes."

Inappropriate Behavior

- Comments that are mean or hurtful, e.g., calling someone ugly, fat, stupid, idiot, etc.

- Offensive jokes, e.g., racist, sexist, phobic, etc.

- Foul language

- Stares at others
- Stands too close to people they do not know
- Touches others inappropriately
- Sexually suggestive comments/advances, e.g., nudity, masturbation, sexually insinuating remarks
- Physical or verbal threats
- Lacks modesty, e.g., urinates or takes clothes off in public
- Spits, belches, or does other embarrassing things in social situations
- Uncontrolled impulses
- Inappropriate reactions to situations, screams or shouts without warning
- Talks to strangers about personal matters
- Unwarranted accusations
- Extreme emotional outbursts and overreactions

These behaviors may occur frequently and at high volume. Behaviors vary because people vary. It is important to identify behaviors and personality changes. Proper identification enables the process of establishing interventions and re-directional techniques that will be successful for future situations. It is imperative to attempt to understand why and when the behaviors are occurring, e.g., are they more frequent in the morning/evening/all day, are they related to demands not being met immediately? Unlocking the meaning behind some of these behaviors or implementing successful interventions will assist you to provide the best care possible. A good method to tracking and understanding your loved one's behaviors is to keep a behavior journal or behavior log. Document all behaviors that you encounter to include: time of day, specific behavior, successful and unsuccessful interventions. Accurate tracking of behaviors will assist caregivers, family, and friends that work with your loved one to provide a successful and consistent behavior management plan with documentation to support approaches and interventions that work and those that don't.

There is no sugar coating. The fact is that any of the changes described can occur, and they can be challenging and embarrassing for you.

When armed with knowledge and techniques, you, your loved one, and all caregivers can still experience joy. You can decrease the negative effects of frontotemporal dementia as much as possible.

As a caregiver of someone with frontotemporal dementia, support is extremely important for both the individual and family members.

Chapter 2

Activities, Their Benefits, and Help You Bring In

"Activities" and "Activities of Daily Living" (ADLs) are critical aspects to caring for a loved one at home. Both leisure and daily living activities require knowledge of your loved one's habits, preferences, abilities, and routines. Caregivers need to have the ability to communicate with and execute a planned activity with your loved one. Unplanned things happen to us in life, but all activities should be planned to offer the best possible outcome to enhance your loved one's sense of well-being. Activities should promote or enhance your loved one's physical, cognitive, and emotional health. In this book, we will focus on leisure activities and the activities of daily living with common sense approaches. We will offer suggestions and tips on the "How To's" of getting your loved one engaged, dressed, and fed.

15

In the institutional setting of today, leisure
activities are required by law if a nursing home
accepts government funding. In these
situations, activities are to be provided to
every resident on a daily basis based on an
individual's preferences. Activities has grown
into a profession where Certified Activity
Professionals and their staff plan and execute
activity programs for residents and seniors in
their care. It is NOT just bingo.

In addition, staff members are required to
undergo annual training on the basics of
Activities of Daily Living in order to provide
better care for the residents they work with.

This book was made for the millions of
families and informal caregivers who care for
their loved ones with frontotemporal
dementia at home. Recognizing the growth in
the numbers of those aging in place due to
financial need or desire to just be at home, the
R.O.S. Activities 101/201 Programs and this
book are based on the principles and

approaches used by the professionals
in skilled settings. This was done for
two reasons.

1. Provide family caregivers the knowledge
    and tools to allow them to engage their
    loved one so that both can enjoy the
    benefits of activities.
2. Offer a starting point that will provide
    continuity of approach, care,
    communication, and information-gathering
    to minimize changes and acclimation time
    if your loved one does have to move from
    home to an institutional setting.

If you choose to use the services of a home
care agency while caring for your loved one at
home, please ask if they have a Home Care
Certified professional on staff and make sure
that the caregiver you choose has received
basic training on Leisure Activities and
Activities of Daily Living. This will assist with
continuity of approach, communication, and
planning that will benefit both you and your
loved one.

Our goal is to help you deliver meaningful programs of interest to your loved one that focus on physical, social, spiritual, cognitive, and recreational activities. Everyone involved in the care for your loved one should be "on the same page" to minimize changes and challenges that your loved one will face.

Not all family members may understand or accept your loved one's dementia. Your loved one may look the same on the outside and might be having a "good day" when someone comes to visit. Family members who visit occasionally may not understand or see all of the symptoms that primary caregivers see daily. They may underestimate or minimize the responsibilities or stress. This can create conflict. If it helps to avoid a conflict or stress, please have the family members read this book prior to a visit so they can begin to understand the monumental task that you face as a caregiver.

It can take a while to learn new roles and responsibilities. It is critical, however, to have as many family members and friends involved in your loved one's life as possible. This is not just to show your loved one they are cared for and loved, but also to give you, the primary family caregiver, the occasional and much-needed break.

The importance of understanding your family dynamics and the importance of each role an individual plays in the family will lead to better understanding and comprehension for the future. As the dementia progresses, roles will evolve, and everyone needs to understand that this is a process.

Whether family members come for an occasional visit or visit regularly every week, each can play an important role in your loved one's life. Family members can help with caregiving, preparing the home to ensure safety and quality of life, and successfully engaging with your loved one.

The Benefits of Activities
with a Standard Approach

Caregiver Benefits of Standard Approach to Activities

Planned and well-executed activities result in less stress for the caregiver as well as less stress for your loved one. Whether it is playing a game or bathing, a standard approach where as many details are planned as possible, can make a significant, positive difference for everyone.

Social Benefits of Activities

Activities offer the opportunity for increased social interaction between family members, friends, caregivers, and the one being cared for. Activities create positive experiences and memories for everyone.

Behavioral Benefits of Activities

Well-planned and well-executed activities of any type can reduce challenging behaviors that sometimes arise when caring for someone with dementia.

Self-Esteem Benefits of Activities

Leisure activities offered at the right skill level provide your loved one with an opportunity for success. This is also true with Activities of Daily Living such as dressing. Success during activities improves how your loved one feels about themselves.

Sleep Benefits of Activities

As part of a daily routine, activities can improve sleeping at night. If a loved one is inactive all day, it is likely they will nap periodically. Napping can interrupt good sleep patterns at night.

Being a primary caregiver is a 24/7 job. Without help, you are always on call and run the risk of becoming physically and mentally exhausted.

When you do bring in help, make sure all of your loved one's caregivers (full-time, part-time, family, and friends) use the same approach for activities and interaction that you do. With a common approach, there are significantly less opportunities to disrupt routines and make unsettling changes that affect you and your loved one long after the help has left.

A common approach is key. Demand it!

The Four Pillars of Activities

The R.O.S. Activities 101/201 Programs focus on the Four Pillars of Activities. These are areas that all caregivers for your loved one should be familiar with to provide continuity of care and give your loved one the greatest opportunity for success to engage and improve the quality of life for everyone.

First Pillar of Activities: Know your Loved One—Information Gathering and Assessment

Have a Personal History Form completed. Know them—who they are, who they were, and what their functional abilities are today. Make sure all caregivers know this as well.

Second Pillar of Activities: Communicating and Motivating for Success

Communication is key. Each caregiver must know how to effectively communicate with your loved one and be consistent with techniques.

Third Pillar of Activities: Customary Routines and Preferences

As best as possible, maintain a routine and daily plan based on your loved one's needs and preferences.

Fourth Pillar of Activities: Planning and Executing Activities

Based on all of the information you have gathered about your loved one, you have the opportunity to offer engaging activities that are appropriate and meet your loved one's personal preferences.

Chapter 3

First Pillar of Activities:
Know Your Loved One—
Information Gathering
and Assessment

Information gathering and assessment is the First Pillar of Activities.

What does your loved one enjoy doing?

What do you need to provide care?

Is your loved one capable of doing something independently?

This may vary greatly from what they could do prior to the onset of frontotemporal dementia and may change frequently.

Caregivers

Who is your loved one the most comfortable with when needing care? Female/male, a specific caregiver?

Sex and age of the caregiver can be a significant issue. Here is an example of why: A 90-year-old female might be horrified if a 20-year-old male family member came into the bathroom to assist with care. She may fear for her safety or be embarrassed depending on her level of dementia. It is important to establish this as soon as possible. It may take some trial runs with various care providers until it becomes clear who your loved one is the most comfortable with. This can also shift and your loved one may want a female to provide intimate care such as grooming, bathing, dressing, and toileting. However, they may want a male to provide assistance in mobility, transfers, and cooking.

Illnesses and Limitations

What physical illness or limitations does your loved one have? What type of modifications are needed, if any? These, in addition to the personal history information, are just as important to know so that all caregivers can provide the highest level of care.

As you can see from the example, details matter. Gather as much information as you can for yourself and all caregivers who may help your loved one.

Basic knowledge about your loved one is essential. The little things matter.

There are two important items that you should take note of.

First, any form that is used to gather personal history should be a living document. It needs constant updating as the dementia progresses. It is also important to remember that with dementia, what works today won't work tomorrow, and may not work five minutes from now! For example, your loved one asked for their favorite food for dinner, changed their mind after the food was placed in front of them, and then yelled at you for not getting them food when they were hungry.

Second, you and your loved one may have been very private people. Having dementia will change that. Gathering information and sharing with other caregivers is critical. Your loved one's past pleasures, likes, and activities will become cornerstones of the communication process for everyone.

It is important that before you begin providing personal care, you first need to recognize various personal attributes and abilities of your loved one and yourself. The more you know about your loved one's lifestyle, likes, and dislikes, the easier providing for their personal and leisure needs will be.

If there is something that you might consider embarrassing or private and choose not to share what happened years ago, please note that one way or another, it will come out.

Whatever it was that you think is difficult to share, caregivers, and family members that offer assistance are not there to judge you or your loved one on something that happened years or even decades ago. They are there to help you in your moment of need today. Information is vital to the communication process and allows all caregivers the opportunity to turn a "bad" day into a "good" day through proper communication techniques.

As the primary caregiver, you may already know most of the answers, but this is a good and necessary exercise for you, other family members, and other caregivers to execute. We suggest everyone fill out the R.O.S. Personal History Form which comes later in this section and is also available for download at www.ROSTherapySystems.com. As a starting point, you, the primary caregiver, are most likely able to provide the following basic information:

Basic Information

- Name, preferred name to be called, age, and date of birth

Background Information

- Place of birth, cultural/ethnic background, marital status, children (how many, and their names), religion/church, military service/employment, education level, and primary language spoken

Medical and Dietary/Nutritional Information

- Any formal diagnosis, allergies, and food regimen/diets

Habits

- Drinking/alcohol, smoking, exercise, and other things that are a daily habit

Physical Status

- Abilities/limitations, visual aids, hearing deficits, speech, communication, hand dominance, and mobility/gait

Mental Status

- Alertness, cognitive abilities/limitations, orientation to family, time, place, person, routine, etc.

Social Status

- One-on-one interaction, being visited, communicating with others through written word or phone calls, other means

Emotional Status

- Level of contentment, outgoing/withdrawn, extroverted/introverted, dependent/independent

Leisure Status

- Past, present, and possible future interests

Vision Status

- Any impairment they may have

Personal History Form

This is _____'s Personal History

Name: _____

Maiden Name: _____

Date of Birth: _____

Preferred Name: _____

Name and relationship of people completing this history:

_____

_____

_____

What age do you think the person thinks they are?

_____

Do they ask for their spouse but do not recognize them?

_____

Do they look for their children but do not recognize them?

_____

Do they look for their mom? _____

Do they perceive themselves as younger? Please describe.

_____

_____

Describe the "home" they remember. _____

_____

_____

_____

Describe the person's personality prior to the onset of dementia. _____

_____

_____

What makes the person feel valued? Talents, occupation, accomplishments, family, etc. _____

_____

_____

What are some favorite items they must always have in sight or close by? _____

_____

_____

What is their exact morning routine?

_____

_____

_____

_____

What is their exact evening routine?

_____

_____

_____

_____

What type of clothing do they prefer? Do they like to choose their own clothes for the day or do they prefer to have their clothes laid out for them?

_____

_____

_____

_____

What is their favorite beverage?

_____

What is their favorite food?

_____

What will get them motivated? (Church, friends coming over, going out, etc.)

_____

_____

_____

_____

List significant interests in their life, such as hobbies, recreational activities, job related skills/experiences, military experience, etc.

- Age 8 to 20:

_____

_____

_____

- Age 20 to 40:

_____

_____

_____

What is their religious background? (Affiliation, prayer time, symbols, traditions, church/synagogue name, etc. Did they lead any services or sing in the choir?)

_____

_____

_____

What type of music do they enjoy listening to, playing, or singing? Do they have any musical talents?

_____

_____

_____

What is their favorite TV program? Movie?

_____

_____

_____

Did they enjoy reading? Which authors, topics, or genres do they prefer? Would they listen to audiobooks or books on tape?

_____

_____

_____

_____

Can they tell the difference between someone on TV and a real person?

_____

_____

Marital status - If married more than once, provide specifics. Include names of spouses, dates of marriage, and other relevant information.

_____

_____

_____

_____

_____

List distinct characteristics about their spouse(s), such as occupations, personality traits, or daily routine.

_____

_____

_____

_____

_____

Do they have children? Be sure to include children both living and deceased. Include names, birth dates, and any other relevant information.

_____

_____

_____

_____

_____

Who do they ask for the most? What is their relationship with this person(s)? Describe how that person typically spends their day.

_____

_____

_____

_____

_____

What causes your loved one stress?

_____

_____

_____

_____

What calms them down when they are stressed or agitated?

_____

_____

_____

_____

Other information that would help bring joy to your loved one.

_____

_____

_____

_____

_____

_____

_____

_____

_____

Functional Levels

In addition to the Personal History Form, you also need to look at your loved one's functional level. When planning meaningful activities based on individual interests, you need to also consider your loved one's functional abilities. Focus on what they can do and set them up for success based on what they are able to accomplish. There are several definitions of functional levels. For the purposes of this topic, we will address the following four functioning levels:

Level 1

Your loved one has good social skills. They are able to communicate. They are alert and oriented to person, place and time, and they have a long attention span.

Level 2

Your loved one has less social skills, and their verbal skills may be impaired as well. Your loved one may have some behavior symptoms. They may need something to do, and may have an increased energy level, but they have a shorter attention span.

Level 3

Your loved one has less social skills. Their verbal skills are even more impaired than they were at Level 2. They are also easily distracted. Your loved one may have some visual/spatial perception and balance concerns, and they need maximum assistance with their care.

Level 4

Your loved one has a low energy level, nonverbal communication skills, and they rarely initiate contact with others, however, they may respond if given time and cues.

With the personal history and functional level information, you and every caregiver have the greatest opportunity to provide person-appropriate activities for your loved one.

Chapter 4

Second Pillar of Activities: Communicating and Motivating for Success

Communicating and motivating is the Second Pillar for success in engaging in an activity with your loved one. Because communication and approaches will become difficult early in frontotemporal dementia, recognizing your loved one's ability to understand what is being said is significant to your success in caregiving.

The key to effective communication is the ability to listen attentively with your ears and eyes and using the knowledge of your loved one's lifestyle and habits.

Remember, being logical and/or arguing with your loved one won't work, and in fact could make the situation worse.

Your loved one may not be able to process their environment or what they are doing at any given moment, but they are constantly reading and reacting to your facial expressions, tone of voice, and body language.

Effective Communication Techniques

- Be patient and calm. Use a warm, gentle tone of voice.

- Talk to them like an adult.

- Always smile. Look directly at your loved one.

- Speak slowly with words they know. Use short, simple sentences. Repeat as you need to.

- Give one instruction at a time. Repeat as often as needed.

- Gently touch or hold your loved one's hand while talking, if tolerated.

- Complete one step at a time.

- When they finish one step, go to the next.

- Repeat steps as needed.

- When your loved one is trying to communicate, stop what you are doing, and really listen to what they are <u>trying</u> to tell you.

- Give time for your loved one to do or answer.

- Turn questions into statements:

  Instead of, "Do you have to go to the bathroom?" Change to, "The bathroom is right here."

  Instead of, "Would you like a sandwich?" Change to, "Your favorite sandwich is ready."

  Instead of, "Do you want to watch TV?" Change to, "Look, your favorite show is on."

The point of this is that decision making and judgment are often impaired. Limiting options makes choosing easier. You want to guide your loved one.

Working with Existing Impairment

- If your loved one has a hearing impairment, you will have to speak louder or write in large print. Make sure they are facing you. Make sure if they wear a hearing aide, it is on, and they use it. The trick will be to speak louder without your loved one feeling like you are yelling at them.

- If your loved one cannot see because of a visual impairment, be sure to use verbal cues to let them know you are engaged.

Being a Detective

As your loved one's dementia progresses, there will be many days that you will not know what kind of day it will be until after it has started. If there is an issue, the starting point in your process is communicating to figure out what they are telling you.

Approaches to Successful Communication

Be Calm

Always approach your loved one in a relaxed and calm demeanor. Your mood will be mirrored by your loved one. Smiles are contagious.

Be Flexible

There is no right or wrong way of completing a task. Offer praise and encouragement for the effort your loved one puts into a task. If you see your loved one becoming overwhelmed or frustrated, stop the task, and re-approach at another time.

Be Nonresistive

Don't force tasks on your loved one. Adults do not want to be told, "No!" or told what to do. The power of suggestion goes a long way, and you get more with an ounce of sugar than you do a pound of vinegar.

Be Guiding, but Not Controlling

Always use a soft, gentle approach, and remember your tone of voice. Your facial expressions must match the words you are saying.

Suggested Approaches with FTD— The "Do's" and "Don'ts"

Important "Do's"

- **Do** be patient.

- **Do** stop and take a deep breath.

- **Do** allow your loved one to cool down when they become angry before you continue what you are doing.

- **Do** engage in a conversation with your loved one about something they enjoy.

- **Do** identify and shift their focus away from a "trigger" behind a behavior. (A trigger is the reason for the way they are acting.)

- The radio or TV may be too much stimulation.
- They may not recognize a visitor in the house.
- They may be afraid.

- **Do** remain calm.

- **Do** use silence selectively.

- **Do** give yourself a time-out, if possible, when you feel yourself getting tired, frustrated and/or angry.

- **Do** maintain your loved one's schedule as close and as long as possible, but at the same time be flexible when behaviors occur.

- **Do** monitor to see if a task or activity becomes too overwhelming. It can lead to anger, frustration, and irritability for your loved one. Discontinue the task/activity with the possibility of returning to it later, and offer alternative tasks/activities.

Important "Don'ts"

- **Don't** try to reason, argue or explain "why."

- **Don't** show anger or dissatisfaction.

- **Don't** retaliate or show aggressive body language.

- **Don't** use baby talk.

- **Don't** ask, "Do you remember?"

- **Don't** make demands of them.

- **Don't** correct them or say, "I told you so!"

Things to Remember

- Just because your loved one may shake their head yes or no during a discussion, does not always mean your loved one understands or even hears what you or another caregiver is saying. Your loved one may not want to admit they have not understood or heard you.

- All caregivers need to use communication techniques that provide an open, nonthreatening environment for your loved one.

- Behavior can either enhance and encourage communication or shut down communication altogether. You need to assess your listening style and be able to assess the listening styles of the other caregivers and family members working with your loved one.

- It is imperative that all caregivers working with your loved one are on the same page and aware of behaviors, triggers, routines, interventions, and daily tasks.

Chapter 5

Third Pillar of Activities:
Customary Routines
and Preferences

Customary routines and preferences is the
Third Pillar in an activities program. With
frontotemporal dementia, customary daily
living and preferences may change when
least expected.

Caregiving is a daily routine. The goal is to
gain from your loved one's perspective how
important certain aspects of care and activity
are. This will be difficult. As their abilities
to communicate and engage in their
environment decreases, your loved one's
past interests may no longer be pertinent.

When caring for your loved one at home,
this very well could mean a disruption to
your personal daily routine with behavioral
issues of your loved one becoming very
wearing for you.

Daily Customary Routine

Your loved one has distinct lifestyle
preferences and routines. They should be
preserved to the greatest extent possible with
frontotemporal dementia. All reasonable
accommodation should be made to maintain
their lifestyle preferences.

Always understand that longtime preferences
may change as a result of the FTD.

With frontotemporal dementia, depression
can be a major concern early on. This needs to
be recognized and treated.

Even though changes to lifelong preferences
may occur, your loved one's lifestyle
preferences and routine still need to be
accommodated as much as possible. When
a person feels like their control has
been removed and that their preferences
are not respected as an individual, it can
be demoralizing.

Activity Preferences

Activities are a way for individuals to establish meaning in their lives.

A lack of opportunity to engage in meaningful and enjoyable activities can result in boredom, depression, and behavioral disturbances.

Individuals vary in the activities they prefer, reflecting unique personalities, past interests, perceived environmental constraints, religious and cultural background, and changing physical and mental abilities. Remember these can and will change with FTD. That is why we use the Personal History Form as a starting point and then engage with Lesson Plans, which are covered in the following chapter. Both of these are intended to be living documents for all caregivers to use, update, and learn from.

With frontotemporal dementia, behaviors and perceptions will interfere with established daily routine.

Let us look at an example of a daily routine and how this type of dementia may alter the usual routine.

You have been a full-time caregiver for Margaret. You have been able to maintain a relatively normal schedule for both of you while making adjustments as needed based on the progression of the dementia.

Margaret had always been a quiet woman who never used profanity or spoke badly about anyone. One day, you are in the kitchen when you realize that Margaret is at the window yelling and swearing at the postman to get off her property. You try to quiet Margaret and reason with her when she turns around and directs her foul language toward you. After a week of this, you suddenly realize that this behavior is from frontotemporal dementia. It is important to realize that you have not done anything wrong and Margaret's behavior is from her disease, not the people around her.

Your encounters with Margaret as well as others will change, and you will need to adjust and help others, such as the postman, to understand and not become angry.

A helpful intervention for this scenario is to determine the time frame that the postman delivers mail at Margaret's home. Use this time daily with Margaret to engage in a task or activity away from the view of the outside, and eliminate the behavior through redirection.

Chapter 6

Fourth Pillar of Activities: Planning and Executing Activities

Planning and executing is the Fourth Pillar in engaging a loved one in an activity. With the knowledge of your loved one's history, functional level, effective communication techniques to use, and their daily routine, we now look at planning activities in which they can be successful.

The Lesson Plan

The Lesson Plan template is a guideline for an activity. Each loved one's abilities and responses are different. This will dictate how you modify an activity to meet their individual needs and abilities. The Lesson Plan is an ever-changing document. It is meant to be written on to note any changes needed so the next person working with your loved one can follow your modifications in hopes of recreating a positive experience.

Items in the Lesson Plan

Date

Document the date the program is used.

Program Name

You can rename the program if you or your loved one prefer.

Objective of Activity

Our goal is to provide meaningful activities. People have a need to be productive and they want to engage in something with a purpose. List the objectives of the program.

Materials

The list of suggested materials to use with this program.

Prerequisite Skills

The skills your loved one needs to participate in this program.

Activity Outline

Step-by-step instructions to complete this program.

Evaluation

When you or a family member are conducting an activity with your loved one, documenting results and responses are critical to improve activity programs for your loved one. Items to document:

- Verbal cues, physical assistance or modifications you make to activity.

- Your loved one's response to this program.

- Did your loved one enjoy this activity or not?

- Was the activity successful at distracting or eliminating a negative behavior?

A blank template is included on the next page to give you an example of what a Lesson Plan looks like.

Lesson Plan Blank Example

Date	Program Name

Objective of Activity

Materials

Prerequisite Skills

Activity Outline

Evaluation

Chapter 7

Leisure Activity Categories, Types, Topics, and Tips

Activity Categories

Activities are generally broken down into three different categories:

Maintenance Activities

Maintenance activities are traditional activities that help your loved one to maintain physical, cognitive, social, spiritual, and emotional health.

Examples include: using manipulative games such as those in the R.O.S. Legacy™ System, craft and art activities, attending church services, working trivia and crossword puzzles like the *How Much Do You Know About* puzzles, taking a walk, and tai chi.

Supportive Activities

Supportive activities are for those that have a lower tolerance for traditional activities. These types of activities provide a comfortable environment while providing stimulation or solace.

Examples include: listening to and singing music, hand massages, relaxation activities such as aromatherapy, meditation, and bird-watching.

Empowering Activities

Empowering activities help your loved one attain self-respect by receiving opportunities for self-expression and responsibility.

Examples include: cooking, making memory boxes, and folding laundry.

Activity Types

Once you have chosen an activity from a category that will suit your loved one's need, you must choose an activity type that will interest them. There are several types of activities to choose from. Below are some examples:

Art Activities

- Coloring
- Painting
- Dancing

Craft Activities

- Jewelry making
- Knitting
- Scrapbooking

Verbal Activities

- Conversation
- Trivia

Entertainment Activities

- Board games, card games
- Video games
- Crossword puzzles

Listening Activities

- Music
- Storytelling
- Books on tape
- Listening to the radio

Visual Activities

- Watching a movie
- Watching a performance

Writing Activities

- Writing a story or poem
- Writing a letter

Active Activities

- Dancing
- Folding laundry
- Road trips

Activity Topics

Once you know what type of activity you want to engage your loved one from, here are some suggestions for topics the activity can be based on:

Colors

- Colors of their favorite sports team
- Colors of their wedding
- Colors of flowers or cars

Music

- Favorite music
- Music from when they were younger and dating
- Patriotic songs
- Holiday songs
- Favorite artists from the age they think they are, e.g., if they believe they are 25 years old, use popular singers or songs of that era.

Military Service

- War stories
- World events of their time
- Their personal experiences of either military service or what it was like in the States

Holidays

- Specific holidays that coincide with their culture or religion
- Favorite holidays

Cooking

- Home cooking
- Comfort food
- Favorite recipes from their mother/grandmother
- Favorite food associated with events, holidays, family gatherings

Sports

- Professional sports teams they liked
- Their involvement in sports
- Big sporting events from their era

School Days

- Where they went to school
- Favorite school classes or teachers
- Memories of their children's school events

Old Cars

- Their family's first car
- Their first car
- Prices of cars now and then
- Dream cars

Places

- Where they were born
- Where they grew up
- Places they have been
- Vacations they took

Activity Tips for Individuals with Mild to Moderate Dementia

Many loved ones have cognitive deficits that are significant enough to impact their day as well as their awareness of their surroundings.

By providing activities that reinforce their past, we increase and improve their social skills which can improve their general interactions with others.

Validating Activities

Validating activities validate the memories and feelings of individuals who are much disoriented. They focus on your loved one's perception of what happened in the past.

Reminiscing Activities

Reminiscing activities are designed to help your loved one identify the important contributions he or she has made throughout their lifetime. It is an important part of human development to see oneself as a contributing member of society.

Resocializing Activities

Once your loved one can successfully participate in reminiscing and validating activities, it is time to encourage them, through resocializing activities, to build on those social skills and begin to expand their connections to the community in which they live. This can be as simple as with a neighbor, in church, or within their community.

Chapter 8

Activities of Daily Living
Tips and Suggestions

Unlike leisure activities, the Activities of Daily Living covered in this book are necessary activities that are a part of everyday life. As you work to adjust your loved one's daily routine, here are some practical tips and suggestions to work into the daily routine concerning the basic ADLs.

Bathing

Bathing can be a relaxing, enjoyable experience or a time of confrontation and anger. For individuals that suffer from any form of dementia, bathing/showering can be a traumatic experience. Use a calm approach. Your loved one's "usual" routine is very important. Many attempts and methods may have to be practiced before finding success, relaxation, and a positive experience.

Safety and Preparation

- Water temperature should range from 110-115 degrees Fahrenheit maximum to prevent burning or skin injury.

- Floor of tub needs skid proofing or a rubber mat.

- Place a nonskid rug on the floor outside the tub to prevent slipping.

- Install grab bars around the tub.

- Do not use bath oils.

NEVER leave your loved one unattended in the bathroom.

Bathing—Know Your Loved One

- Are they accustomed to a bath or shower?

- Can they get into a bath or shower without assistance?

- Who is your loved one the most comfortable with when needing care? Female/male, a specific caregiver?

<u>Bathing—Communicating and Motivating</u>

- Don't ask if they want to bathe. Simply say in an easy, friendly voice, "Bath time."

- Use short, simple sentences.

- Look directly at your loved one.

- One step at a time, follow their normal routine. Wash hair first and then wash body, or soak for 10 minutes before washing. When they finish one step, go to the next.

- Be mindful of the little details— preparation and execution.

- Always smile, talk calmly and gently.

- Do not argue, or try to explain "why."

- If your loved one becomes angry or combative about bathing, <u>STOP</u> and try another time.

<u>Bathing—Customary Routines and Preferences</u>

- What time of day does your loved one normally bathe?

- Does your loved one wash their hair or body first?

<u>Bathing—Planning and Executing</u>

- Consider the process that works for the caregiver and loved one when it is time to bathe.

  For example, your loved one needs assistance undressing and getting into the tub. They always remove their shirt first, followed by their pants, socks, and underwear. The tub has a built-in seat that is covered with ceramic tile. Your loved one needs a towel laid on the tile prior to sitting down because the tile is cold against their skin. Once seated, your loved one also likes a towel draped over their shoulders so they feel less exposed with you assisting them while they bathe.

- Have all care items and tools ready prior to starting the bath process.

- Have a shower chair if necessary.

- Have a handheld hose for showering and bathing.

- Have a long-handled sponge or scrubbing brush if they would like to scrub themselves.

- Have sponges with soap inside or a soft soap applicator instead of bar soap. Bar soap can easily slip out of your loved one's hand.

- Take one step at a time. When they finish one step, go to the next.

- Remember to <u>STOP</u> and try another time if your loved one becomes angry or combative.

- Use a towel to put over shoulders or on lap so they feel less exposed.

- Have towel and clothing prepared for when the bath is finished.

- Use a terry cloth robe instead of a towel to dry off.

Other Bathroom & Grooming Activities
Brushing Teeth

- Give them step-by-step directions. This may not be as simple as you think. Take a moment and think of all of the steps necessary to brush your teeth, from walking into the bathroom, to finding the toothpaste in the drawer and removing the cap, to rinsing their mouth once they have finished brushing. Depending on your loved one's level of dementia, it might be easier to show them.

- For family members at home, brush your teeth at the same time.

- Use positive reinforcement, and compliment your loved one on the good job they are doing.

- Help your loved one to clean their dentures as needed.

Shaving

- Encourage a male to shave.

- Use an electric razor for safety.

- If they need assistance, please provide it.

- Give positive feedback, and do not verbally correct.

  For example, if your loved one only managed to shave half of his face, do not criticize and tell him he "did it wrong." Instead ask if he would like some help.

Makeup

- If your loved one had been accustomed to wearing makeup, there is no reason for this to stop. If she shows interest or desire to wear makeup, encourage her to do so, and offer assistance to apply if needed.

Hair

- Try to maintain hairstyle and care as your loved one did.

- Explain each step simply beforehand to reduce any anxiety.

- When washing hair use nonstinging shampoo.

- Use warm water for washing and rinsing. Tell your loved one before you rinse their hair.

Nails

- Keep nails clean and trimmed. Be gentle while trimming your loved one's nails. Be mindful of how you pull and where you place their fingers and arms.

NOTE: It is equally important that caregivers maintain clean, short-trimmed fingernails for safety when providing hands-on care with loved ones.

- If your loved one had a normal/weekly schedule for nail care prior to the onset of dementia or other health issues, please try to maintain that schedule.

- Offer to polish your loved one's nails.

- When polishing, engage your loved one in conversation.

Toileting or Using the Bathroom

- Mark the bathroom door so it can be identified.

- Learn your loved one's individual habits and routines for using the toilet. This may not be something that you know and is part of the changing roles.

- Toilet routinely on rising, before and after meals, and at bedtime, at minimum.

- If your loved one is having trouble communicating, please watch for agitation, pulling at their clothes, walking/pacing restlessly. This may be an indication they need to go to the bathroom.

- Assist with clothing as needed, and be positive and pleasant while assisting.

- Provide verbal cues/instructions as needed, while being guiding, but not controlling as you do.

Clothing

Clothing—Know Your Loved One

- Initially, daily clothing choices should remain as they had been and based on your loved one's available wardrobe.

- As their dementia progresses, changes will have to be made. Clothes need to be comfortable and easy to remove, especially to go to bathroom.

Clothing—Routines and Preferences

- Have a friendly discussion each evening about the next day's schedule and what your loved one may want to wear.

- Remember that as their dementia progresses, changes will have to be made. You may have to limit the choice of clothing and leave only two outfits in their room at a time.

- If your loved one wants to wear the same thing every day, and if you can afford it, buy three or four sets of the same clothing.

- Try to maintain your loved one's preferred dressing routine by laying the clothes out in order of what your loved one prefers to put on first.

Clothing—Planning and Executing

- Choose clothes that are loose fitting and have elastic waistbands.

- Choose wraparound clothing instead of the pullover type.

- You may consider clothing that opens and closes in the front and not the back for your loved one. This may be helpful in allowing them to dress themselves and maintain some independence.

- Choose clothing with large, flat buttons, zippers or Velcro closures.

- If possible, attach a zipper pull to the end of the zipper to make it easier to zip pants or jackets.

- Choose slip-on shoes, and purchase elastic shoelaces that allow shoes to slip on and off without untying the shoelaces.

Dressing

Dressing—Know Your Loved One

Initially, your loved one may just need verbal cues/instructions on dressing. As their dementia progresses you will have to take a more active role. Please remember to allow your loved one to dress themselves as long as possible so they can maintain a sense of dignity and independence. You will have to be the judge of when all caregivers need to begin assisting in the dressing process.

Similar to bathing, you need to identify who your loved one is the most comfortable with when needing care. Female/male, a specific caregiver?

Sex and age of the caregiver can be a significant issue.

Dressing—Communicating and Motivating

- Use short, simple sentences.

- Provide verbal cues/instructions as needed.

- Ask if your loved one would like to go to the toilet before getting dressed.

- If they are confused, give instructions in very short steps, such as, "Now put your arm through the sleeve." It may help to use actions to demonstrate these instructions.

- Give praise as justified for accomplishing each step.

- Always smile, talk calmly and gently.

- Do not argue, or try to explain "why."

- Be guiding, not controlling.

Dressing—Routines and Preferences

- Does your loved one get dressed first thing in the morning—before breakfast or after breakfast?

- Does your loved one change into pajamas right before bed or after dinner?

- Try to maintain your loved one's preferred routine. For example, they may like to put on all of their underwear before putting on anything else.

<u>Dressing—Planning and Executing</u>

- Think about privacy—make sure that blinds or curtains are closed and that no one will walk in and disturb your loved one while they are dressing.

- Make sure the room is warm enough to get dressed in.

- Before handing your loved one their clothes, make sure that items are not inside out and that buttons, zips, and fasteners are all undone.

- Hand your loved one only one item at a time.

- If needed, let your loved one get dressed while sitting in a chair that has armrests. This will help your loved one keep their balance.

DRESSING NOTE 1: If mistakes are made—for example, something is put on the wrong way—be tactful, or find a way for you both to laugh about it.

DRESSING NOTE 2: It can be useful if your loved one wears several layers of thin clothing rather than one thick layer, as they can then remove a layer if they feel too warm.

DRESSING NOTE 3: Remember that your loved one may no longer be able to tell you if they are too hot or cold, so keep an eye out for signs of discomfort.

Meals

General Information

- Limit distractions. Serve meals in quiet surroundings, away from the television and other activities.

- Your loved one might not be able to tell if something is too hot to eat or drink. Always test the temperature of foods and beverages before serving.

- Keep long-standing personal preferences in mind when preparing food. However, be aware that your loved one may suddenly develop new food preferences or reject foods that were liked in the past.

- Give your loved one plenty of time to eat. It may take an hour or longer to finish a snack or meal so factor that into the overall schedule for the day.

- Make meals an enjoyable social event so everyone looks forward to the experience.

Eating

Eating—Know Your Loved One

- Can your loved one feed themselves?

- Does your loved one have a visual impairment that may affect their ability to see their meal or drink?

  NOTE: Older individuals tend to perceive bright, deep colors as lighter. They are able to see yellow, orange, and red more easily than darker colors. Due to change in our eyesight as we age, eating and dining offer additional challenges.

Eating—Communicating and Motivating

- Use short, simple sentences.

- Provide verbal cues/instructions as needed.

- Give your loved one your full attention.

- Always smile, talk calmly and gently.

- Do not argue, or try to explain "why."

Eating—Routines and Preferences

- No matter what time of day they eat breakfast, lunch, and dinner, be consistent every day.

- Offer snacks throughout the day.

- Do they eat their meals at the kitchen table?

Eating—Planning and Execution

Eating a meal can be a challenge for your loved one with dementia. There are several areas that need to be taken into account such as visual impairment, physical ailment, changes in preferences, and dietary restrictions. Here are some simple techniques that can help reduce mealtime problems:

Meal Preparation for Mild Dementia

- If your loved one wants to assist in making a meal:

    - Make sure your cabinets are organized with each item labeled with large easy-to-see labels.

    - Use simple step-by-step written or verbal instructions.

    - You or another caregiver should perform tasks using sharp objects such as knives, or operation of the stove or oven.

    - When using a stove top, use the back burners, and turn the pot handles inward toward the back of the stove to avoid any potential grabbing of the pots or pans.

- If you are not there to supervise because you have to go to work:

  o Avoid planning meals that require use of the stove. Your loved one may not remember to turn off the stove and may not be able to distinguish between a pot that is hot or cold.

  o Lay out the ingredients of a meal on the counter or in the refrigerator in labeled containers in the order that your loved one will use them (similar to laying out their clothes at night).

  o Transfer bulk items, including milk, from a larger container to a smaller container that is easier to lift and pour.

Meal Preparation for Higher Level Dementia

- Try to have all meals eaten at a kitchen or dining table, or in a chair with a serving tray. Avoid meals in bed, if possible. Let the bed be for sleeping.

Appropriate Lighting and Eyesight

- Reduce glare by having your loved one sit with the sunlight behind them when eating.

- Use lighting which illuminates the entire dining space and makes objects visible, as well as reducing shadows or reflections.

- Adjust lighting above the table to help see as much detail as possible.

- Remember that older individuals tend to perceive bright, deep colors as lighter. They are able to see yellow, orange, and red more easily than darker colors.

Setting the Table and Serving

- Set each place setting in the same way for every meal. Set it the way your loved one used to. Offer your loved one the opportunity to assist in setting the table.

- Decide how to set the rest of the table— main dish, side dishes, seasonings, and condiments. Do it the same way each day.

- When pouring a light-colored drink, such as milk, use a dark glass.

- When pouring a dark-colored drink, such as cola, use a white glass.

- Avoid clear glasses. They can disappear from view.

- Use white dishes when eating dark-colored food, and use dark dishes when eating light-colored food.

- To make dishes easier to find on the table, use a tablecloth or placemats that are the opposite color of the dishes.

- Fiesta ware colors (yellow/tangerine) contrast with most foods so they can be easily seen and will enhance visual perception.

- There should be a clear visual distinction between the table, the dishes, and the food.

- Use solid colors with no distracting patterns.

Chapter 9

Home Preparation

Home preparation is an important part of caregiving. The following are general tips that caregivers and family members can use to prepare the home for your loved one.

General Organization and Environment

It is important to remember your loved one's thought process, and how organization is affected.

When organizing your loved one's environment, if you can, do it <u>with</u> them. What works for you, might not work for your loved one.

- Assign everything to a place in the home.

- Always put items back in their place after using them in order to avoid clutter.

- o You may want to go one step further and label drawers and other areas used by your loved one.

- If your loved one has developed problems with motor skills, e.g., walking and balance:

  - o Have your loved one evaluated for the use of a walker or cane.

  - o Remove objects left on the floor, such as shoes, bags, and boxes. These items should be placed in their designated areas of the home. If left out, they can be a tripping hazard.

  - o Keep walkways open and wide.

  - o Use extension cords sparingly, and always secure them out of the places where people walk. Bundle all the cords, and secure them to the wall instead of the floor.

- Remove and avoid clutter on desks, tables, and countertops, and in cabinets and closets. This makes it easier to locate and reach specific items. Your loved one will be less frustrated.

- Install handrails where possible for easier independent movement from one room to the next.

- Leave doors fully opened or closed. Make sure the doors open easily and smoothly and that doorknobs are securely fastened to the door, especially if your loved one has tremors.

- Remove throw rugs. If you must use them, opt for slide-resistant rugs that can be taped or tacked down.

- Identify and address flooring issues. Check every floor, walkway, threshold, and entry. Remove or fix loose floorboards, uneven tiles, loose nails, or carpeting that has bunched up over time.

Furniture

- Make sure there is enough room to move around. If possible, place furniture pieces 5½ feet from each other so your loved one can move comfortably around the room, especially if they are in a wheelchair.

- Use chairs with straight backs, armrests, and firm seats. Where possible, add firm cushions to existing pieces to add height. This will make it easier for your loved one to get up and sit down.

Lighting

Depending on your loved one's eye condition, symptoms from frontotemporal dementia, or individual preference, the need for additional or less lighting could be key in their safety and ability to perform tasks independently.

- If possible, purchase touch lamps or those that can be turned on or off by sound.

- Be certain that all stairwells are well lit and have handrails.

Wandering and Leaving Home without Supervision

You may encounter your loved one attempting to leave to go out for a walk, or believing they need to be somewhere. You may want to install some type of system that will alert you when doors are opened and your loved one may be attempting to leave.

Chapter 10

Review

Activities can improve the quality of life for both you and your loved one. There are many benefits to an Activity Program for your loved one, and you have the opportunity to enjoy them all.

Now that we have gone through the items necessary to put together a successful activity program, the following is a review of the Four Pillars of a successful activity program.

First Pillar of Activities: Know your Loved One—Information Gathering and Assessment

Have a Personal History Form completed. Know them—who they are, who they were, and what their functional abilities are today. Make sure all caregivers know this as well.

Second Pillar of Activities: Communicating and Motivating for Success

Communication is key. Each caregiver must know how to effectively communicate with your loved one and be consistent with techniques.

Third Pillar of Activities: Customary Routines and Preferences

As best as possible, maintain a routine and daily plan based on your loved one's needs and preferences.

Fourth Pillar of Activities: Planning and Executing Activities

Based on all of the information you have gathered about your loved one, you have the opportunity to offer engaging activities that are appropriate and meet your loved one's personal preferences.

About the Authors

Scott Silknitter

Scott Silknitter is the founder of R.O.S. Therapy Systems. He designed and created the R.O.S. Play Therapy™ System, the *How Much Do You Know About* Series of themed activity books and the R.O.S. *BIG Book*. Starting with a simple backyard project to help his mother and father, Scott has dedicated his life to improving the quality of life for all seniors through meaningful education, entertainment, and activities.

Robert D. Brennan, RN, NHA, MS, CDP

Robert Brennan is a Registered Nurse and Nursing Home Administrator with over 35 years of experience in long-term care. He is a Certified Dementia Practitioner and is Credentialed in Montessori-Based Dementia Programming (MBDP) providing general and Train the Trainer programs. Robert was responsible for the development of an Assisted Living Federation of America (ALFA) "Best of the Best" award-winning program for care of individuals with dementia using MBDP. He currently provides education on dementia and long-term regulatory topics.

Vanessa Emm, BA, ACC/EDU, AC-BC, CDP

Vanessa Emm is a certified Activity Consultant and Educator with additional certification as a Certified Dementia Practitioner. Vanessa's background is in Gerontology with an emphasis in biology, research, and grant writing. Vanessa currently serves on the Board of Trustees for the National Association of Activity Professionals.

References

1. *The Handbook of Theories on Aging* (Bengtson et al., 2009)
2. *Activity Keeps Me Going, Volume 1*, (Peckham et al., 2011)
3. *Essentials for the Activity Professional in Long-Term Care* (Lanza, 1997)
4. *Abnormal Psychology*, Butcher
5. www.dhspecialservices.com
6. National Certification Council for Dementia Practitioners www.NCCDP.org
7. "Managing Difficult Dementia Behaviors: An A-B-C Approach" By Carrie Steckl
8. Iowa Geriatric Education Center website, Marianne Smith, PhD, ARNP, BC Assistant Professor University of Iowa College of Nursing
9. *Excerpts taken from "Behavior...Whose Problem is it?" Hommel, 2012
10. *Merriam-Webster's Dictionary*
11. "The Latent Kin Matrix" (Riley, 1983)
12. *Care Planning Cookbook* (Nolta et al.2007)
13. "Long-Term Care" (Blasko et al. 2011)
14. "Success Oriented Programs for the Dementia Client" (Worsley et al 2005)
15. Heerema, Esther. "Eight Reasons Why Meaningful Activities Are Important for People with Dementia." www.about.com
16. *Activities 101 for the Family Caregiver* (Appler-Worsley, Bradshaw, Silknitter)
17. American Foundation for the Blind
18. www.aging.com
19. www.WebMD.com
20. www.caregiver.org

For additional assistance, please contact us at:
www.ROSTherapySystems.com
888-352-9788

57019349R00059

Made in the USA
Columbia, SC
03 May 2019